ETERNAL SPRING
CHI KUNG

*To Scott
with best wishes*

Mar 06

Published by SUNFLOWER PRESS,
P.O. Box 750733, Forest Hills Station, NY 11375

Distributed by Chu Tai Chi
156 W. 44th Street, NY, NY 10036
www.chutaichi.com

Eternal Spring Chi Kung; C.K. Chu
ISBN: 0-9616586-4-9
Library of Congress Control Number: 2002114159

Photography: Charlie Eckert
Design: Noel Claro & Jesse Shadoan

First Edition

ETERNAL SPRING CHI KUNG

CHI KUNG

— C. K. CHU

Other Books By C.K. Chu

Tai Chi Chuan Principles and Practice
The Book of Nei Kung
Chu Meditation

About the Author

Master C. K. Chu developed his system of Eternal Spring Chi Kung through a lifetime of practicing and teaching Tai Chi Chuan and related disciplines at his renowned Times Square martial arts school, Chu Tai Chi (formerly the Tai Chi Chuan Center of New York). Born in Hong Kong in 1937, C. K. Chu holds an M.A. in Physics, which he taught at Queens College (C.U.N.Y.), New York Institute of Technology, and Brooklyn Tech. Master Chu is the author of definitive books on Tai Chi (Tai Chi Chuan Principles and Practice, 1981), Nei Kung (The Book of Nei Kung, 1986), and Taoist meditation (Chu Meditation, 2002), as well as being the creator of Chu Tai Chi: Complete Short Form Instruction & Theory (video, 2000; DVD, 2003). Master Chu is also the founding director of the non-profit Tai Chi Chuan Center (**www.taichichuancenter.org**). For more information, including demonstration videos, visit **www.chutaichi.com**.

For my daughter, Diane

Acknowledgements

I am fortunate to have had the help of my long time student James Borrelli in the conceptualization and writing of this book. I like to think of it as a continuation of an earlier collaboration of ours, *The Book of Nei Kung*, which has been highly praised for its clarity and organized presentation of the subject matter. I believe the same can be said here and the credit for this belongs to Jim. As always, he is able to condense a complex topic into streamlined, elegant text. For these reasons and more, his involvement in this book has been indispensable.

I am also grateful to have had Charlie Eckert as our photographer. His expertise and insights about how to convey Eternal Spring visually were invaluable.

In addition, special thanks go to Noël Claro and Jesse Shadoan for book design and layout; Dimitri Ehrlich and Phillip Corwin for formative editorial guidance in the early stages of the manuscript; Cynthia Elmas for first rate editorial assistance; and Akiko Hikota, Amos Satterlee, Addi Somekh, Kate Wasilewski, and Carol Chu for their help at various stages of production. For careful readings and useful feedback, I also thank Nathaniel Wice, Daniel Zegibe, Hyland Harris, and Kerry McGauran.

A Note of Caution

Before beginning this, or any other exercise program, it is advisable to obtain the approval and recommendation of your health care practitioner. While you are on this, or any other exercise program, you should visit your health care practitioner for periodic monitoring. This program is intended for adults in good health.

Dedication

There is a call for health in the world today. As millions of people move into old age, and many succumb to physical deterioration and debilitating illnesses, there are those among them who seek the wisdom of ancient ways of healing and well-being. It is to those seekers that I dedicate the practice of Eternal Spring Chi Kung.

Table of Contents

Part One: Origins

The Story of Eternal Spring

In 1973 I founded my martial arts school in Times Square, New York City and dedicated it to the classic disciplines of Nei Kung and Tai Chi Chuan. I intentionally chose one of the great crossroads of America as the location for this place of learning so that I could reach the most diverse group of people to share this treasured Chinese heritage.

Over the course of thirty years my efforts have been fruitful. From the many martial arts champions to the innumerable every day students whose lives were dramatically enriched and changed, teaching has given me much fulfillment.

My observation of the general population, however, revealed two significant categories of people which Nei Kung and Tai Chi Chuan could not adequately reach, namely: the elderly and the weak or infirm. I found that these two groups had neither the physical strength to endure the rigors of Nei Kung training, nor the stamina to commit to the length of time and complex learning process of the Tai Chi form.

After years of reflection, I set myself to the task of creating a simple yet highly effective basic discipline that was rooted in my life's work with chi and internal conditioning. This system would be designed for those at the very lowest levels of vitality to give them a bridge back to youth, strength, and well-being.

I named this new system Eternal Spring Chi Kung, and from the very beginning it was an amazing success. From the initial workshops grew classes. From the classes grew the training seminars in which I certified advanced students to teach at numerous New York area community centers, senior citizen centers and nursing homes. And now, as I write these words, plans are being made to bring Eternal Spring to clinics and health care organizations of all types.

Originally conceived for seniors, I was delighted to discover that Eternal Spring also answered a need in many young people who lacked physical conditioning or who did not have the mental discipline necessary to undertake the challenge of Nei Kung or the Tai Chi form. Eternal Spring provided a measured introduction to the specific breathing techniques and the basic alignments which are essential to any understanding of these sophisticated internal martial arts. More importantly, it prepared their minds as well as their bodies, giving them the confidence they needed to graduate on to higher levels of training. Another rewarding revelation has been how well Eternal Spring serves as an overall warm-up for Nei Kung and Tai Chi practice itself. As a result, I have encouraged advanced as well as beginning students to incorporate it into their routines to complete their regimen of training.

Finally, the Eternal Spring system can be further recommended as a practical, efficient, full body preparation for any physical endeavor, whether it be exercise such as aerobics and weight training, or athletics like golf, tennis and team sports.

Chi

The success of Eternal Spring lies in the origins of its twelve forms. Rooted in the fundamental principles of Nei Kung and Tai Chi Chuan, it represents a gentle and reliable guide to cultivate chi in the human body. Simply put, chi is the Chinese word used to describe the life force, the same vital energy which links us to all of nature. The great Taoist sages initiated the study of chi over five thousand years ago. It is the same healing energy that is the basis of acupuncture and traditional Chinese medicine.

Chi kung translates literally as "energy training". Eternal Spring Chi Kung is a system of personal development wherein one can stimulate and accumulate the very life force itself. As such, it is the first step of a wonderful journey to eternal youth.

Longevity and Fitness

The secret to longevity is simply knowing how to correctly maintain the body. Physical fitness is as important as proper diet and nutrition in this process. Regular practice of Eternal Spring is analogous to the sophisticated mechanical maintenance of a high performance luxury car, wherein the engine, brakes, tires and all other systems are constantly tuned up and repaired. Compare such a vehicle to the condition of certain big city taxi cabs which are routinely neglected, run into the ground until their parts wear out and then discarded.

The concept of physical fitness is more subtle than meets the eye. Sometimes the most well-intentioned training strategy can have a negative effect in the long run. People can deceive themselves into thinking they are in good shape when in truth they are merely exercising the external weight bearing muscles of the body, such as the biceps and the quadriceps in order to create a fashionable physique. Others drive the body relentlessly in overly strenuous running or aerobic activity for the sake of some competitive athletic ideal, or to assert a willful spirit of mind over matter. Such extreme emphasis can actually drain away chi and other valuable metabolic resources needed for cleansing, repair and cell replacement within the core of the body.

The path to a sound body lies in balance. The inside must be conditioned as well as the outside. Eternal Spring primarily addresses the internal organs and the joints, which, though they are not visible, still remain the critical determinants of health and mobility.

The abundant chi stimulated by Eternal Spring circulates throughout the entire body down to a cellular level. The steady, relaxed practice of the forms massages all of the internal organs, suffusing them with energy while at the same time toning deep internal muscles which work to keep these organs functioning properly. A well-developed diaphragm muscle, for instance, is essential for the full utilization of the lungs. Other subtle muscle groups are equally important for the kidneys, digestive and sexual organs.

Flexibility of the joints is paramount to mobility. Though the muscles of professional athletes may be chronically tight and sore they can still perform with regularity and proficiency. Joints, however, like the knees, shoulders and lower back, are what most often fail them in the end and terminate their careers. In Eternal Spring, all of the joints of the body are gently and systematically flexed and lubricated. Worn and tired cartilage is repaired and renewed and this greatly increases the strength and resilience of the entire skeletal frame.

The body's internal conditioning is a subject relevant to all of us, not just professional athletes. As one ages, disregarding these fine distinctions of what true fitness is may result in profound changes for the average person. Many individuals who were active and vigorous throughout their lives find themselves suddenly "out of gas." At this stage, the cumulative effect of years without inner maintenance can make them more susceptible to serious illness and some may undergo unexpected physical collapse. I can tell you from personal experience that this does not have to be. I am now sixty-six years old and anyone who knows me will attest to the fact that I maintain the vital life style of a thirty-five-year-old.

Many of my senior students are sharing in this bounty. I constantly hear stories of new flexibility in the lower back, knees, ankles and other joints. I have seen people who were once resigned to a fate of gradual physical deterioration come back to life after just a few classes. One student in his seventies even began playing basketball again. The great secret of the sages is that after healing and recuperation there is growth, even in old age.

As an extra benefit to your well-being, when you practice Eternal Spring, the body's capacity for productive rest is greatly enhanced. You will need less sleep and the sleep that you have will be sound. You will have created for yourself a daily habit of rejuvenation and your life will be far more enjoyable than you ever thought possible.

Goals and Advantages

In summation, Eternal Spring was created with several goals in mind:

- To be a simple practice, easier to learn than the Tai Chi form, but still highly effective.
- To enable an individual to be self-reliant in the cultivation of chi.
- To be accessible to people of all ages and body types regardless of their fitness level.
- To improve strength and overall health.
- To properly align the body and increase range of motion.
- To strengthen the knees and lower back in particular.

In pursuit of these ends, Eternal Spring has many practical advantages:

- It is gentle, and doesn't require any rigorous physical activity such as jumping, bouncing or pounding on the joints.
- It doesn't require equipment or a large space.
- It is easy to remember and easy to practice alone.
- It will fit into any work schedule.

Part Two: Essential Principles

Breath

Breath is the first necessity of life. We can go without food for over thirty days, and without water for three or four days; but we cannot last more than a few minutes without air.

Since ancient times, the great sages and founding masters of the Chinese healing arts have known that the breath is the vehicle for chi. As we age, our breath often becomes shallow and less efficient; it requires more effort, yet less air enters the lungs. The gradual deterioration of this primary body function contributes to a progressive loss of vitality.

Correct breathing is essential to good health. As mentioned above, Eternal Spring is designed to develop specific internal muscles, such as the diaphragm and lower abdominals, to greatly increase lung capacity and efficiency, and thus greatly enhance the accumulation of chi.

Eternal Spring emphasizes breathing through the nose when executing the forms according to the following four principles: "Long, Deep, Small, and Smooth."

- Long: each inhalation and exhalation is executed slowly and for an extended duration of time.
- Deep: the breath is pulled down in a vertical direction to the lower abdomen.
- Small: only a small quantity of air is utilized at a time.
- Smooth: the breath is continuous with no pause between inhalation and exhalation.

Imagine you have a new balloon that you wish to inflate. To fill it, you slowly introduce a small quantity of air a bit at a time so the balloon will expand evenly without bursting. The same principle holds true for the lungs. When you practice Eternal Spring breathing, it ensures that the lungs will develop uniformly and gradually without straining delicate membranes that have been constricted by years of disuse. This method guarantees that they grow stronger in a natural, healthy way.

Alignment

The specific placement of the various parts of the body in the Eternal Spring forms are called alignments. These alignments amplify the chi brought into the system by the breath and stimulate it to circulate freely and in great abundance throughout a network of internal pathways known as meridians. Attention paid to the exact positioning of the feet, pelvis, torso, arms and head has a profound and dynamic effect on this distribution process. In effect, the practice becomes a powerful self-administered acupuncture treatment.

The application of these alignments represents the accumulated knowledge of my lifetime practicing and teaching Nei Kung and Tai Chi Chuan. Derived from these ancient internal martial arts, the subtle forms of Eternal Spring promote cellular regeneration throughout the body from the skin to the internal organs and structural elements within.

As a result, Eternal Spring increases bone density, which is good for people of all ages, but is especially important for the elderly. It builds ligament, tendon and structural muscle tissue, enabling the individual to maintain correct body posture continually. Many students report feeling solid, centered and more stable on their feet in just a short period of time.

Mind

Mental focus is essential in any endeavor, and in particular when dealing with physical conditioning. When practicing Eternal Spring it is necessary to adopt an attitude of relaxed discipline. The mind should become a friendly observer and partner to the process, rather than a drill sergeant or a coach.

As you approach the forms, suspend self-criticism and judgment. Feel your way into the various alignments. Listen to your body; don't push it or force it to do what you want it to do. Awareness is the guiding principle to correct performance. Correct performance, not blind willpower, is the path to the chi.

Observe the effect of each of the forms with the quiet part of your mind. Think of a Chinese fan unfolding, each section opening in sequence, gradually revealing the pattern of a hidden image. Eternal Spring has been designed in the same way; each form engaging and stimulating multiple channels of internal meridians, building one upon the other in sequence until the full flower of chi is experienced.

Between forms, become passive, go into repose and be open to the sensations awakening within. The chi knows where to travel naturally much better than you can direct it. Let it flow in you like rain water, trickling through the leaves and branches of a tree, all the way down to the dry thirsty roots deep in the ground.

Part Three: The Forms

The following points should be emphasized when executing the forms:

- Breathe through the nose, not the mouth (except Form 5, Roaring Lion).
- Feel your way into the alignments, don't force them.
- Pause between the forms to swing the arms and shake the hands gently several times.
- Focus the mind inward.

Form 1: Dragon Claws

Warm Up: Stretch the palms and the fingers open as wide as possible and hold for five seconds. Slowly clench the open hands into firm claws and hold for five seconds. Continue to clench the clawed hands into tight fists and hold for five seconds. **Repeat this sequence ten times.**

1 Stand in a neutral stance with the feet apart, shoulder width and parallel.

2 Clasp the hands together behind your back like interlocking claws with the knuckles facing down.

2 side view   **3** side view

3 INHALE. Gently tilt the head back and clasp the clawed hands as tightly as possible. Pull the shoulders back as far as possible, drawing the shoulder blades toward each other. Allow the torso to lean back and stretch to the limit while you inhale as much as possible from the lower abdomen.

4 EXHALE. Return to a normal standing position and relax. Keep the hands gently clasped until you execute the next breathing sequence. **Repeat steps #3 and #4 ten times.**

Form 2: Fish Leaps Up

1 Stand in the neutral stance with the feet apart, shoulder width and parallel.

2 Hold the right hand palm facing up with the thumb folded inward. Press all four fingertips of the right hand firmly into the lower abdomen at a point about two inches below the navel.

3 Place the left hand on the back of the right one to help pull it inward.

2 side view   **3** top view

4 INHALE. Imagine being slowly lifted up from the top of the head. As you lift up, raise the heels steadily off the floor until you are balanced on the toes and balls of the feet. Relax as you inhale, expanding the lower abdomen as much as possible. Do not lift up the shoulders.

5 EXHALE. Slowly return the heels to the floor into a normal standing position.
Repeat steps #4 and #5 ten times.

Form 3: Yawning Lion

1 Stand in the neutral stance with the feet apart, shoulder width and parallel.

2 Hold the right hand palm facing up with the thumb folded inward. Press all four fingertips of the right hand firmly into the lower abdomen at a point about two inches below the navel.

3 Place the left hand on the back of the right one to help pull it inward.

4 detail

4 INHALE. Relax the abdomen, letting it expand as much as possible as it pushes the fingers outward. Continue to inhale and lean backward as far as you can. When it feels like you have inhaled to the limit, give the inhalation an extra push, just like giving a pump the final push when you inflate a bicycle tire.

5 EXHALE. Pull the palm and fingers of the right hand inward deeply. The lower abdomen will slowly collapse and deflate, causing you to bend forward. As the abdomen deflates further continue to bend forward to the limit while exhaling as much as possible. When you think you have exhaled to the limit, give an extra pull with the hand and exhale a bit more.
Repeat steps #4 and #5 ten times.

Form 4: Sleeping Lion

1 Stand in the neutral stance with the feet apart, shoulder width and parallel.

2 Fold the arms loosely in front of the chest.

2 side view   **3** side view

3   Slowly bend forward from the waist so that the torso is hanging down and the elbows are pointing toward the floor. The legs should be straight. Allow the body to relax into the pull of gravity. Close the eyes. **Remain in this position for thirty-six slow deep breaths.**

Form 5: Roaring Lion

1 Stand in the neutral stance with the feet apart, shoulder width and parallel.

2 Hold the right hand palm facing up with the thumb folded inward. Press all four fingertips of the right hand firmly into the lower abdomen at a point about two inches below the navel.

3 Place the left hand on the back of the right one to help pull it inward.

5 detail

4 Make the sound HING and let the force of the expanding abdomen push the hands out from the body as you lean back.

5 Swing the hands back to the lower abdomen making the sound HAR as soon as the fingers hit the same point two inches below the navel where they started from; and lean forward.

Repeat steps #4 and #5 ten times.

Form 6: Frog Stance

1 Stand in the neutral stance with the feet apart, shoulder width and parallel.

2 Put the hands on the hips.

3 Gently pull the elbows forward bringing the chest to a concave shape as you bend the knees and slowly lean forward from the waist.

Adjust the height of the stance according to your ability:

A) Beginner   B) Intermediate   C) Advanced

4   Continue leaning forward, bending the knees outward and forward until you are touching the floor with the fingertips of both hands. The feet need to be flat with the heels touching the floor at all times. Keep the hands on the floor, using them *only* to balance yourself as you continue to bring the knees forward and outward. Position the torso parallel to the floor as much as possible. **Hold this position for thirty-six long, slow deep breaths.**

Form 7: Golden Rooster

1 Stand in the neutral stance with the feet apart, shoulder width and parallel.

2 Bend the knees and tuck in the pelvis.

3 INHALE. Slowly lift the left knee in front of you as high as possible while keeping the right foot flat and steady on the floor. At the same time, lift the left hand in front of you, so that the palm is facing to the right as you bring the left elbow to touch the rising left knee. Continue to inhale for as long as possible while holding this position.

Note: For those who are not yet strong enough or who have not developed a good sense of balance, Golden Rooster can be performed with the use of a wall or a piece of furniture for support.

4 EXHALE. Lower the left hand and knee back to step #2.

5 INHALE. Slowly lift the right knee in front of you as high as possible while keeping the left foot flat and steady on the floor. At the same time, lift the right hand in front of you, so that the palm is facing to the left as you bring the right elbow to touch the rising right knee. Continue to inhale for as long as possible while holding this position.

6 EXHALE. Lower the right hand and knee back to step #2.
Repeat steps #3, #4, #5 and #6 ten times.

Form 8a: Crane Stretches Wings (forward)

1 Ready position: Stand in the neutral stance with the feet apart, shoulder width and parallel. Cross the arms at the wrists in front of the chest, with the right hand outside and the palms facing inward. The hands should not touch the chest. Make sure the elbows and shoulders are relaxed.

2 Pull the arms back lifting the elbows up, high and outward without raising the shoulders.

1 side view

2 side view

3 side view

3 INHALE. Push the hands all the way forward to the limit, rotating them so that the palms face forward.

4 EXHALE. Reverse the movement. Pull the hands back lifting the elbows up, high and outward as in step #2.
Repeat steps #3 and #4 ten times slowly, then ten times fast.

Form 8b: Crane Stretches Wings (sideways)

1 Ready position.

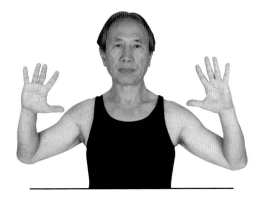

2 INHALE. Open the chest, bringing the hands around to both sides of the torso.

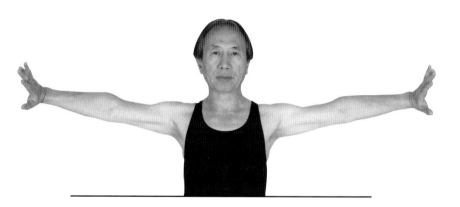

3   Continue to INHALE, rotating the hands so that the palms face outward to the sides as you push them all the way to the limit.

4   EXHALE. Reverse the movement, closing the chest and returning the hands to the front as in step #1.
Repeat steps #2, #3 and #4 ten times slowly, then ten times fast.

Form 8c: Crane Stretches Wings (upward)

1 Ready position.

2 INHALE. Pull the arms back lifting the elbows up, high and outward without raising the shoulders.

3 side view

3 Continue to INHALE as you lean back and push the hands all the way up to the limit, rotating them so that the palms face upward with the fingertips of either hand opposing each other.

4 EXHALE. Pull the hands down and return them to the front as in step #1.
Repeat steps #2, #3 and #4 ten times slowly, then ten times fast.

Form 9: Shifting Frog

1 Stand in the neutral stance with the feet apart, shoulder width and parallel.

2 Slowly lean forward from the waist while bending the knees until you are touching the floor with both palms. The feet need to be flat with the heels touching the floor at all times.

5 Gradually shift back to the center and then to the left. Straighten the right leg and execute the same alignments as you sink down on the left side.
Slowly shift from one side to the other ten times.

2 side view

3 Gradually slide the feet farther apart until they are about three times the shoulder width, while pointing the toes outward about thirty degrees. Keep the hands on the floor, but only use them to balance yourself as you adjust most of the weight to the feet.

4 Shift to the right, straightening the left leg while sinking down as much as possible onto the right side. Keep both feet flat on the floor. Make sure the knees are not bending inward, and don't arch the lower back. Hold the position for about ten seconds.

Form 10: Easy Horse Stance

1 Stand in the neutral stance with the feet apart, shoulder width and parallel.

2 Put the hands on the hips.

3 side view   **4** side view

3 Lean forward. Gently pull the elbows forward bringing the chest to a concave shape.

4 Tuck in the pelvis, and slowly bend the knees by bringing them forward and outward until they hang over the toes. It is important to keep the heels on the floor, and not to arch the lower back.

Relax and hold the position for thirty-six slow, deep breaths.

Form 11: Tai Chi Opening

1 Assume the Easy Horse Stance.

2 Drop the hands and let the arms hang loosely at the sides.

3 INHALE. Raise the hands in front of you up to shoulder level, with the fingertips loosely pointing downward. The elbows should be bent slightly.

4 Continue to INHALE while raising the hands so that the fingers point forward.

5 EXHALE. Bend the elbows, and pull the hands back toward the chest, level with the shoulders. The wrists and fingers should be relaxed.

6 INHALE. Lift the hands slowly so that the fingers point up, and the palms face each other.

7 EXHALE. Drop the hands slowly downward, keeping the fingers pointing upward, the wrists bent, and the palms facing each other.

8 Drop the hands. **Repeat steps #3 through #8 ten times.**

Form 12: Pivoting Into Bow Stances

1 Assume the Easy Horse Stance.

2 Shift the weight to the left. Make sure the weight is always on the outer edge of the left foot.

3 Turn the torso to the right, lift up the right foot with the toes pointing upward and pivot 90 degrees to the right.

4 Step down on the right foot and shift the torso on to it, making sure the weight is always on the outer edge of the foot.

9 Shift the weight to the left foot by picking up the right heel. The pelvis should remain tucked in.

10 Pick up the right foot and draw it in while maintaining the same height.

11 Slowly place the right foot down, heel first, out to the right.

5 Pick up the left foot and draw it in while maintaining the same height.

6 Slowly place the left foot down, heel first, out to the left.

7 Step down on the left foot and slowly push the torso off the right heel until the weight is distributed 50% onto each foot.

8 Continue pushing off the right heel and turn the toes of the right foot inward about 70 degrees as the torso turns to the left. When you finish, you should have about 70% of the weight on the left leg and 30% on the right. The weight should be on the outer edges of the feet, which should be spaced slightly wider than shoulder width. The pelvis should face forward. This is called Left Bow Stance.

2 Step down on the right foot and slowly push the torso off the left heel until the weight is distributed 50% onto each foot.

13 Continue pushing off the left heel and turn the toes of the left foot inward about 70 degrees as the torso turns to the right. When you finish, you should have about 70% of the weight on the right leg and 30% on the left. The weight should be on the outer edges of the feet, which should be spaced slightly wider than shoulder width. The pelvis should face forward. This is called Right Bow Stance.
Repeat #1 through #13 ten times.

Part Four: Practice

Mental Attitude

Approach the practice of Eternal Spring with a spirit of opportunity rather than obligation. Keep in mind that you don't need a great deal of strength or will power to perform these simple but powerful forms. You need only set aside the time to gently begin. Understand further that this is without a doubt one of the most beneficial expenditures of your time that you could engage in for the health of your body.

Acknowledge the mental resistance, if you have any, and just assume the neutral stance. Slowly commence Dragon Claws. Once you begin to stimulate the flow of chi, the body will come alive. As the body recognizes the delight of the energy, the mind will soon follow and then urge you on rather than fight with you. If you are not strong now I assure you this new skill can gradually carry you far beyond your current limitations to states of well-being you are not yet aware of.

Training Program

The Eternal Spring Chi Kung series can be completed comfortably in one hour. The best time to do it is first thing in the morning on an empty stomach. If you are hungry have a glass of water, not juice. If you practice later in the day, don't eat heavily up to an hour before. I also suggest that you do Eternal Spring before any other type of exercise.

I recommend that **Beginners** perform the entire series **a minimum of two times a week for six months.**

Individuals at an **Intermediate** level should perform the series **every other day for a year.** During each session single out a form you feel the least proficient at and do it more than the standard prescribed number of ten repetitions. Gradually increase your capacity for all the forms over a period of time in increments of five repetitions to a maximum of thirty-six.

At an **Advanced** level, do the series **every day**. Continue to single out an individual form each session and perfect it.

For those who are already practitioners of Nei Kung and Tai Chi Chuan, please note that, by design, the sequence of the Eternal Spring forms ends with the beginning of the Tai Chi form itself. This was intentional on my part so as to lead the individual to the doorway of this next level of development.

Accordingly, I recommend that every student of Nei Kung and Tai Chi Chuan utilize Eternal Spring as a means to prepare for and optimize their practice by warming up and instantly circulating the chi. In this regard, the forms should be done in order but with limited repetition and duration, to save time.

About the Tai Chi Chuan Center

The Tai Chi Chuan Center is a not-for-profit organization focused on promoting the health of mind, body and spirit in our community through the practice of Eternal Spring Chi Kung, Nei Kung, Tai Chi Chuan, Meditation and related arts. Please contact us for more information at:

Tai Chi Chuan Center
156 West 44th Street
New York, NY 10036
(212) 221-7333

office@taichichuancenter.org
www.taichichuancenter.org

Eternal Spring Chi Kung Classes and Teacher Training Program

The Tai Chi Chuan Center offers regular Eternal Spring Chi Kung classes in its New York studio and through its community outreach programs at New York-area community centers, senior centers, and nursing homes. In addition to supporting the development of Eternal Spring Chi Kung, the Tai Chi Chuan Center also trains Eternal Spring teachers.

Please check our website or otherwise contact us for more information.

How to Support the Activities of TCCC

The Tai Chi Chuan Center is a 501(c)(3) not-for-profit charitable organization. We are grateful for any contributions in support of our operating costs, curriculum development and outreach activities. Please make checks payable to Tai Chi Chuan Center. We can also accept credit card contributions through our website, **www.taichichuancenter.org**.